Shining Brass

Book 2, Grades 4 & 5

Piano Accompaniment E♭

For use with

E♭ Soprano Cornet · E♭ Horn · E♭ Bass · E♭ Tuba

Composers

Tom Davoren, John Frith, Timothy Jackson, Peter Meechan,
Lucy Pankhurst and David A. Stowell

Project consultant

Nicky Daw

ABRSM

First published in 2012 by ABRSM (Publishing) Ltd, a wholly owned subsidiary of ABRSM,
24 Portland Place, London W1B 1LU, United Kingdom

Reprinted in 2012, 2014

© 2012 by The Associated Board of the Royal Schools of Music
ISBN 978 1 84849 446 6
AB 3700

A CIP catalogue for this book is available from The British Library.

Cover design by www.adamhaystudio.com
Music origination by Andrew Jones
Printed in England by Caligraving Ltd, Thetford, Norfolk

With particular thanks to Alan Bullard for his contribution to this project.

Contents

(Pianists should note that the solo line printed above the accompaniment reproduces the 𝄞 Brass part.)

Beaufort Allegro

Tom Davoren

★ The mordents in the solo part are optional and not required in an ABRSM exam.

6

Folk Song

Lucy Pankhurst

★ The trills are optional and not required in an ABRSM exam.

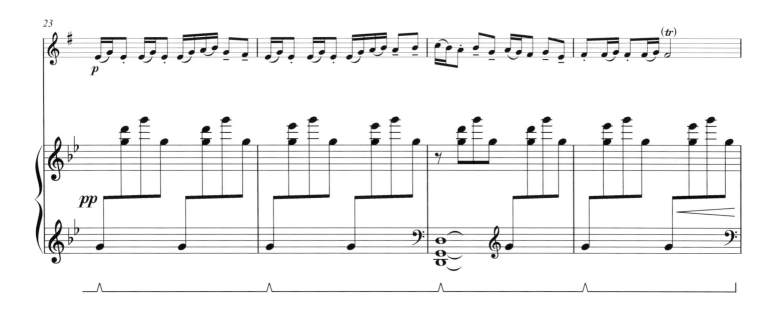

Jiggedy Jig

John Frith

Bragtime

John Frith

Open Plains

David A. Stowell

Way Down South

Peter Meechan

Caber Dance

John Frith

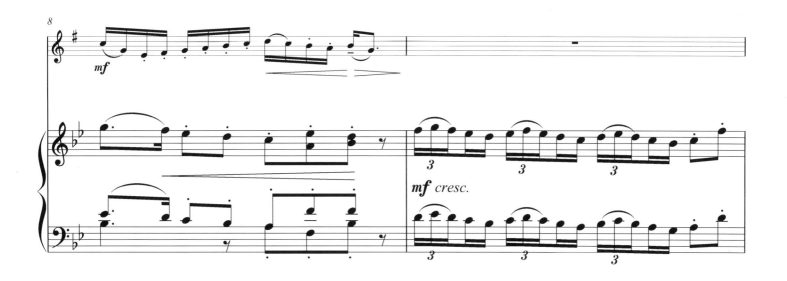

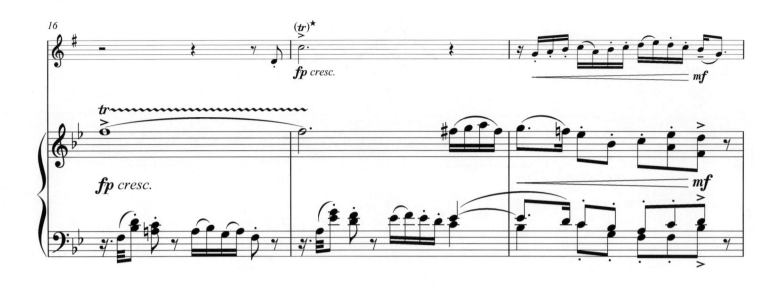

★ The trills are optional and not required in an ABRSM exam.

Canzona

John Frith

Jam Bouree

David A. Stowell

★ Notes and ornaments in brackets are optional and not required in an ABRSM exam. The bracketed notes can be treated as optional breath marks.

Final Thought

Peter Meechan

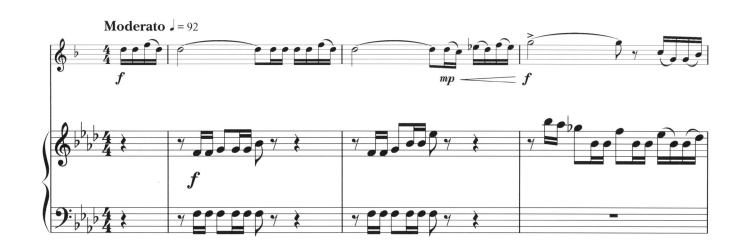

poco a poco agitato

Più mosso ♩. = 48

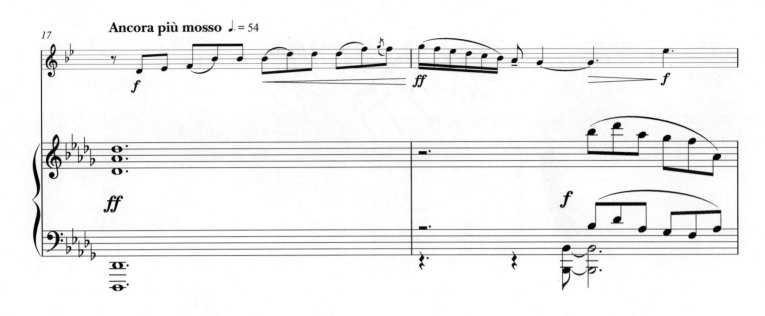

for Lindy Tennent-Brown

Lindy Hop!

Tom Davoren